HOWLING HOWARD

Written by Deborah M. Newton Chocolate ▪ Illustrated by Ken Spengler

MODERN CURRICULUM PRESS

PROJECT DIRECTOR: Susan Cornell Poskanzer
ART DIRECTOR: Lisa Olsson

MODERN CURRICULUM PRESS
13900 Prospect Road, Cleveland, Ohio 44136

Simon & Schuster • A Paramount Communications Company

This edition is published simultaneously in Canada by
Globe/Modern Curriculum Press, Toronto.

ISBN 0-8136-1148-2 (STY PK)   ISBN 0-8136-1149-0 (BB)   ISBN 0-8136-1150-4 (SB)

10 9 8 7 6 5 4 3 2   96 95 94 93

There once was an old dog named Howard who lived with a boy named Mike Brown. And this is the tale of how Howard caused trouble for one part of town.

Old Howard began to howl loudly
each day as the bright sun went down.
The howling got louder and louder
till Howard woke up the whole town.

When Mike Brown went out to see Howard
he said to him, "Howard, what's wrong?"
But Howard just howled a lot louder.
He howled and he howled all night long.

One evening the block had a meeting.
The council said, "We can't allow
this howling of Howard's to happen.
This howling must stop here and now."

So the next day the Browns left Howard with an uncle on Third Street and Dow. Mike said to him, "Don't worry, Howard. I'll get you back somehow."

Well, Howard didn't like Uncle Powell's.
The apartment was in such a tizzy!
When Howard tried clowning and pouncing,
Mike's uncle was always too busy.

Meanwhile Mike Brown was scouting.
He asked all the neighbors around,
"What could have caused Howard's howling?
What could have scared that old hound?"

Poor Howard dreamed of his doghouse.
He dreamed of his hound friends uptown.
And most of all Howard the howler
dreamed of his best friend, Mike Brown.

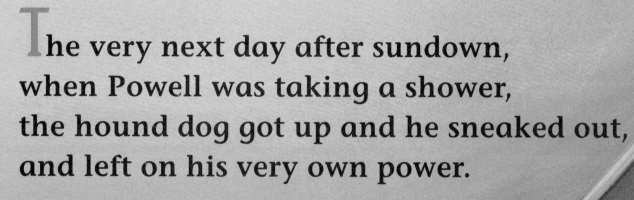

The very next day after sundown,
when Powell was taking a shower,
the hound dog got up and he sneaked out,
and left on his very own power.

Mike Brown was still out there scouting.
He put his young nose to the ground.
He found something light and quite fluffy,
but he wasn't sure WHAT he had found.

That night he stayed on the lookout.
He listened for every small sound.
And at last in the silvery moonlight,
he saw something flying around.

And then came a very loud howling.
It sounded a lot like a hound's.
And Mike turned around to find Howard,
sitting there crouched on the ground!

He said to his dog, "Listen, Howard,
I found out what's making you howl.
The terrible thing that you saw here?
It's a bird — a little screech owl!"

And so Howard came out of hiding.
He watched as the bird settled down.
He was happy to be in his doghouse.
He was glad to be home with Mike Brown.

Howard made friends with that screech owl.
He learned to get over his fright.
And now all the neighbors are happy
because Howard stopped howling at night.

HOWARD
AND
OWL